IMAGINE THAT

Licensed exclusively to Imagine That Publishing Ltd
Tide Mill Way, Woodbridge, Suffolk, IP12 1AP, UK
www.imaginethat.com
Copyright © 2018 Imagine That Group Ltd
All rights reserved
0 2 4 6 8 9 7 5 3 1
Manufactured in China

Written by Oakley Graham
Illustrated by Alexia Orkrania & Mr Henry Fisher

ISBN 978-1-80105-166-8

A catalogue record for this book is available from the British Library

When I Dream of 123

Written by OAKLEY GRAHAM

Illustrated by ALEXIA ORKRANIA & MR HENRY FISHER

1 polar bear

Polar bears are big and white, and can sometimes be a bit grumpy. If you meet a grumpy polar bear, build a funny snowman to cheer him up.

2 wizards

Wizards are jolly fellows with long grey beards and pointy hats. Wizards cannot hear very well on account of all the hair growing out of their ears.

3 hippos

Hippos have very sensitive skin and love wallowing in oozy mud. If you ever see a sunburnt hippo, try not to laugh as this can make them turn even redder.

4 dinosaurs

Dinosaurs are very good at hiding and so everyone thinks they are extinct. If you find a dinosaur hiding under your bed, it is best to sleep somewhere else.

5 princesses

Princesses are very pretty and like
to wear long dresses when they go out
shopping. Some princesses kiss frogs
to see if they will turn into a handsome prince.

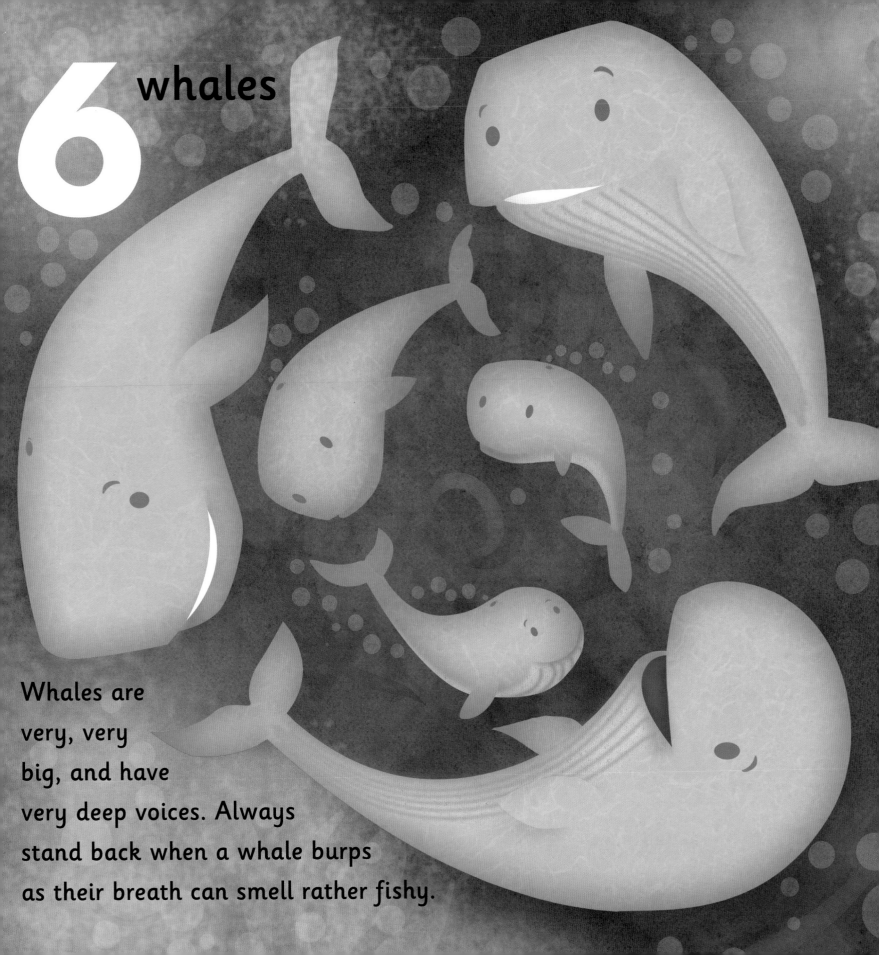

6 whales

Whales are
very, very
big, and have
very deep voices. Always
stand back when a whale burps
as their breath can smell rather fishy.

7 pirates

All pirates have pet parrots and mostly wear pyjamas. Pirates love to fight and never say sorry.

8 penguins

Penguins like two things: sliding and swimming. Because they have large feet, they are very good at both.

9 teddy bears

Teddy bears are kind and cuddlesome. They meet up with their friends when you are asleep and like to eat custard sandwiches.

10 ladybirds

Most ladybirds are bright red with black spots. Despite their name, not all ladybirds are ladies, and no ladybirds are birds.

11 meerkats

Meerkats like eating crunchy bugs
and wrestling. Because of this,
their burrows tend to be
rather messy.

12 hot-air balloons

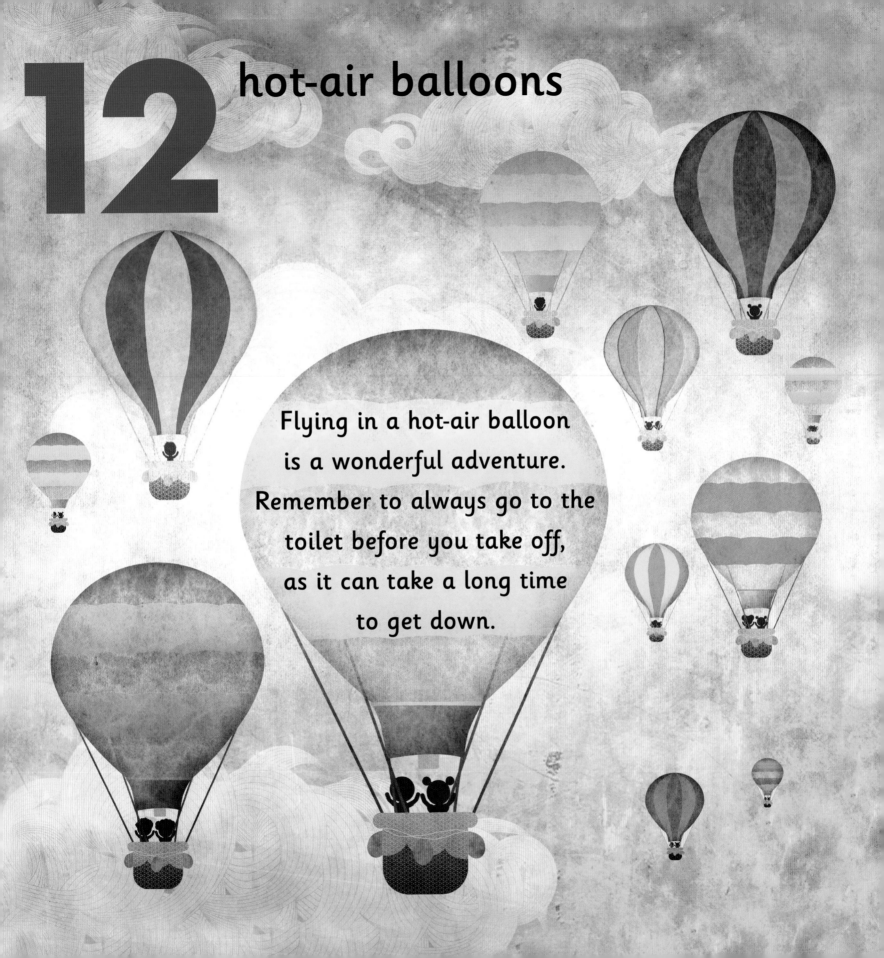

Flying in a hot-air balloon is a wonderful adventure. Remember to always go to the toilet before you take off, as it can take a long time to get down.

13 dolphins

Dolphins live in
the sea and eat fish.
Dolphins love to tell jokes and
they brush their teeth three times a day.

14 clouds

Clouds come in lots
of different shapes, colours and sizes. Although they
sometimes look fluffy and pink, they do not taste like candyfloss.

15 seahorses

Seahorses like two things: swimming forwards and swimming backwards. Because they are rather small, they never get very far.

16 pixies

Pixies are the same size as a daisy and have lots of freckles. If you are quick enough to count a pixie's freckles, it will grant you a wish.

17
diamonds

Diamonds always sparkle and twinkle in the light.
Most queens have lots of diamonds and get very cross
if the king does not buy them more for their birthday.

18

jellies

Jellies are made from special wobbly ingredients. Despite being so wobbly, jellies don't fall over very often and taste great with ice cream.

19 books

All books have a beginning, a middle and an end. It is best to start reading a book at the beginning, followed by the middle and then finish at the end.

20 rabbits

Rabbits have big, floppy ears and like to work with magicians. Make sure that you have a good supply of carrots if you invite a rabbit to a party.

30

sheep

Sheep look like fluffy clouds
with legs. On account of sheep being
rather boring, if you have trouble
sleeping it is recommended that you
try counting them.

40

goblins

Goblins are small and green and
very naughty. Most goblins eat
with their fingers and never say
please or thank you.

50

clownfish

Clownfish do not dress in funny
clothes or do silly things to make
you laugh. Despite their name,
they are nothing like real clowns at all.